GRIMMY™

WHAT A WAG

Mike Peters

RAVETTE BOOKS

First published by Ravette Books Limited 1993

Printed and bound for Ravette Books Limited,
Egmont House, 8 Clifford Street,
London W1X 1RB.
An Egmont Company
by Proost International Bookproduction, Belgium.

ISBN: 1 85304 405 9

THIS IS AWFUL, WE'RE TRAPPED HERE IN THE VET'S OFFICE 18 FLOORS UP.
WILL YOU RELAX, HE'S A VET. HE'S HERE TO HELP US.

...IF THERE'S ANYTHING WRONG WITH US, THE VET WILL HAVE US FIXED.

© 1989 Grimmy Inc.
Distributed By Tribune Media Services
4/10

HEY, WHO OPENED THIS WINDOW?

FIXED, ATTILA, THEY'RE GOING TO HAVE US FIXED!

I KNOW IT... DOGS CAN SENSE THESE THINGS... THAT'S WHY SHE BROUGHT US HERE TO THE VET.

© 1989 Grimmy Inc.
Distributed By Tribune Media Services

I DON'T WANT TO BE FIXED...

...I WANT TO STAY BROKEN.
4-11

THIS IS AWFUL... HERE I AM.. COLD, FRIGHTENED, HYSTERICAL...

AT THE END OF MY WITS, TOTALLY STRUNG OUT, STANDING ON THE LEDGE OF A BUILDING...

..AND NOW SOME DOCTOR IS GOING TO HAVE ME NEUTERED...
© 1989 Grimmy Inc.
Distributed By Tribune Media Services
4/12

I THINK I SAW THIS ONCE ON GERALDO.

GOOD GOD.. THAT YELLOW DOG IS OUT ON THE LEDGE. THIS COULD RUIN ME!!!

HEEERE, DOGGIE, DOGGIE, DOGGIE
4/13

© 1989 Grimmy Inc.
Distributed By Tribune Media Services
?
ZIP

SLAM
!

OK, THE VET'S LOCKED OUTSIDE, NOW'S OUR CHANCE TO ESCAPE.. BUT WE'VE GOT TO GET PAST THE NURSE.

AND HOW ARE WE GOING TO DO THAT?
EASY... GIVE ME SOME SOAP.
© 1989 Grimmy Inc.
Distributed By Tribune Media Services

OKAY, DOG.. OPEN UP, WHAT HAVE YOU GOT IN THERE?
VET
4-14

RABIES!

RABIES!
VET
4-15

RABIES!

WELL, I PUT ANOTHER DIME IN THE METER.. I WONDER IF THE VET HAS GOTTEN AROUND TO SEE GRIMM YET?
© 1989 Grimmy Inc.
Distributed By Tribune Media Services

...YEP, HE'S SEEN HIM.

THAT'S THE LAST TIME I FEED THE PARAKEET STEROIDS...
4-17
© 1989 Grimmy Inc.
Distributed By Tribune Media Services

GRIMMY, YOU DID IT... YOU ACTUALLY DRANK OUT OF YOUR WATER BOWL!
GRIMM
© 1989 Grimmy Inc.
Distributed By Tribune Media Services
FOR THE FIRST TIME YOU DIDN'T DRINK OUT OF THE TOILET, YOU USED YOUR OWN DISH!!!
...I MUST'VE HAD AN OUT-OF-POTTY EXPERIENCE.
GRIMM

GRIMMY, WOULD YOU PLEASE TAKE OUT THE TRASH ?...
4/19
GERALDO

!
GERALDO
© 1989 Grimmy Inc.
Distributed By Tribune Media Services

EXCUSE ME... DO YOU HAVE A WINE LIST?
TRASH
© 1989 Grimmy Inc.
Distributed By Tribune Media Services
4-20

© 1989 Grimmy Inc.
Distributed By Tribune Media Services
OH OH... HE CAUGHT ME RELATING THE ACCOUNTS OF A GAME WITHOUT THE EXPRESSED WRITTEN CONSENT OF MAJOR LEAGUE BASEBALL...
OG
TCHER
4/21

LADIES AND GENTLEMEN, CHILDREN OF ALL AGES...
OH OH... THE FLEA CIRCUS IS IN TOWN.
4/22
© 1989 Grimmy Inc.
Distributed By Tribune Media Services

I WEIGH 30...
© 1988 Tribune Media Services, Inc.
All Rights Reserved

..THAT'S 210 IN DOG POUNDS.

OH BOY..IT'S MY FAVORITE SOAP OPERA...
© 1989 Grimmy Inc.
Distributed By Tribune Media Services

..DOG DAYS OF OUR LIVES.

© 1989 Grimmy Inc.
Distributed By Tribune Media Services

ZING

A CAT IS A DOG'S HOME ENTERTAINMENT CENTER.

WE'VE GOT TO BE FRIENDS, ATTILA. Y'KNOW, YOU'RE SORT OF LIKE A BROTHER TO ME...
© 1989 Grimmy Inc.
Distributed By Tribune Media Services

...A BROTHER WHO'S BEEN FORCED TO WEAR A REALLY DISGUSTING LOOKING CAT FUR.

MUNCH, MUNCH, MUNCH,
GRIMM

GRIMM
©1989 Grimmy Inc.
Distributed By Tribune Media Services
4-28

GRRRRRR
RRRRRRR
RRRRRRRRR
GRIMM

I'M SORRY YOU HAD TO SEE THAT,
GRIMM

©1989 Grimmy Inc.
Distributed By Tribune Media Services
4-29
WAKE UP! THIS IS THE GREATEST DREAM I EVER HAD...

INSTEAD OF A MAILMAN... I CAUGHT THE POSTMASTER GENERAL,

OH MY GOODNESS, I MISSED YOUR BIRTHDAY, GRIMMY, LETS SEE... YOU'RE A LITTLE OVER FOUR YEARS OLD NOW,

...THAT MAKES YOU ABOUT THIRTY IN DOG YEARS,
©1989 Grimmy Inc.
Distributed By Tribune Media Services
5-1

THIRTY! I CAN'T BE THIRTY!!

I HAVEN'T EVEN HAD ZITS YET,

I'M THIRTY IN DOG YEARS.. I DON'T BELIEVE IT...

I'M THE ONLY THIRTY-YEAR-OLD GUY WHO STILL HASN'T GONE THROUGH PUBERTY...

©1989 Grimmy Inc.
Distributed By Tribune Media Services
...I MEAN BESIDES MICHAEL J. FOX,
5-2

HOW COULD I BE THIRTY IN DOG YEARS?

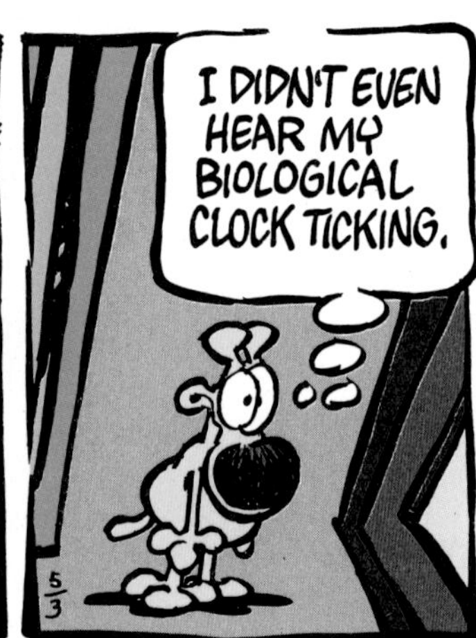
I DIDN'T EVEN HEAR MY BIOLOGICAL CLOCK TICKING.
5/3

...MAYBE MY BIOLOGICAL CLOCK IS DIGITAL.

IT'S UNBELIEVABLE, I'M THIRTY YEARS OLD, BUT I DON'T LOOK IT.

I STILL HAVE THAT SAME YOUNG, ADORABLE FACE AS I DID WHEN I WAS FOUR...

I WONDER IF CLIFF RICHARD DOES THIS EVERY NIGHT.?
5-4

I CAN'T BE THIRTY, I'M ONLY FOUR.. I'M STILL A PUPPY...

LOOK, PUPPIES LIKE PLAYING WITH YARN, SEE I'M A PUPPY... GOO, GOO, GAA..

GOO GOO... DA DA, GAA GAA, GOO GOO, DAA DAA, GAA.. ER.. OOPS...
5-5

...I'M NOT GETTING OLDER, I'M GETTING SENILE.

5-6
ZOOM

BONK

GRIMM, WHAT ARE YOU DOING?

..IT'S BETTER TO BURN OUT THAN TO RUST OUT.

IS GRIMMY GETTING OVER THE FACT THAT HE'S THIRTY?
5/8

OH, YEAH... HE SPENT ALL YESTERDAY LOOKING FOR WRINKLES AND AGE SPOTS. BUT I'M SURE HE'S GOTTEN OVER IT...

Rx
I THINK THIS DOG WANTS SOME RETIN-A.
© 1989 Grimmy Inc. Distributed By Tribune Media Services

GRIMMY... LOOK AT THIS MESS ALL OVER THE SOFA!

THIS HAPPENS EVERY SPRING... I HATE WHEN YOU START SHEDDING.

WHEN YOU'RE THIRTY, IT'S NOT CALLED SHEDDING...
© 1989 Grimmy Inc. Distributed By Tribune Media Services
5-9

...IT'S CALLED MALE PATTERNED BALDNESS.

I BLEW IT... I LOST MY CHILDHOOD. ALL THOSE PRECIOUS MOMENTS...

I WENT THROUGH THE BEST YEARS OF MY LIFE WITHOUT EVEN KNOWING IT.
© 1989 Grimmy Inc. Distributed By Tribune Media Services

REMEMBER, ATTILA, IN LIFE, YOU ONLY GO AROUND...
5/10

...NINE TIMES.
I HATE CATS.

I'M THIRTY YEARS OLD, AND LOOK AT ALL THE THINGS I'VE MISSED... I'VE NEVER PLAYED BASEBALL...

I'VE NEVER DOUBLE DATED.. I'VE NEVER GIVEN ANYONE A HICKEY...
5-11
© 1989 Grimmy Inc. Distributed By Tribune Media Services

DON'T EVEN THINK ABOUT IT.

ATTILA, I'M GOING TO RECAPTURE MY YOUTH AND MAKE UP FOR LOST TIME...

AND EXPERIENCE EVERYTHING I'VE MISSED IN MY CHILDHOOD...
© 1989 Grimmy Inc. Distributed By Tribune Media Services

AND JUST HOW ARE WE GOING TO DO THAT, RIN TIN TIN?
5/12

RALPH, THERE'S A DOG OUTSIDE THROWING ROLLS OF TOILET PAPER IN OUR ELM TREE.

I CAN'T BELIEVE IT. I'M THIRTY IN DOG YEARS. MY BODY IS FALLING APART.
© 1989 Grimmy Inc. Distributed By Tribune Media Services

...EVERY SECOND I'M GETTING OLDER AND OLDER.
5-13
TICK TOCK, TICK TOCK, TICK TOCK, TICK TOCK...

TICK, TOCK, TICK,
PLEASE, NOT DURING PEE WEE HERMAN.

LOOK, GRIMMY, IT'S ONE OF YOUR SISTER'S PUPPIES...HIS NAME IS REX.

ISN'T HE ADORABLE? WE'RE GOING TO BABY-SIT HIM FOR A WHILE. I LOVE HOW HE GOES "YIP."
YIP YIP YIP YIP
5-15

YIP YIP YIP YIP YIP YIP YIP YIP YIP
© 1989 Grimmy Inc. Distributed By Tribune Media Services

I GUESS "YIP" IS PUPPY FOR "COO."
YIP YIP YIP

OH NO...THAT LITTLE PUPPY IS MAKING MESSES ALL OVER THE FLOOR...
5/16
THERE ARE STAINS AND SPOTS EVERYWHERE... HE'S TURNED THIS PLACE INTO A DISASTER AREA...

WE'VE GOT TO STOP..AH, ER.. SAY, WHAT IS HIS NAME AGAIN?
© 1989 Grimmy Inc. Distributed By Tribune Media Services

REX... BUT I CALL HIM REXXON.
YIP YIP YIP YIP

NO, NO, REXXON, WIDOW PUPPY-KINS JUST MADE ANOTHER MESSY. MUMMY DOESN'T WIKE MESSIES...

MUMMY IS TWY-ING TO KEEP THE HOUSE QWEEN... UNDER-STAND, BOO-BOO-KINS?

YUCK... HE DID IT AGAIN!
5/17

© 1989 Grimmy Inc. Distributed By Tribune Media Services
SOMETIMES, WIDOW REXXON JUST CAN'T HELP IT.

WELL, REXXON, YOU SURE HAVE MADE A MESS OF THINGS.

THERE ARE SPOTS AND SPILLS ALL OVER AND IT'S GOT TO BE CLEANED UP...
© 1989 Grimmy Inc. Distributed By Tribune Media Services

..NOW WHAT DO YOU SUGGEST TO DO FIRST?

NO... NOT HIRE A P.R. FIRM.
5/18

YUCK!.. LOOK WHAT YOU'VE DONE TO THE FLOOR...

I'M SORRY, REXXON, BUT YOU'VE CREATED THIS MESS, NOW YOU'RE GOING TO HAVE TO CLEAN IT UP...

© 1989 Grimmy Inc. Distributed By Tribune Media Services

YIP YIP YIP YIP YIP YIP
5-19

HE SAID NOT UNTIL THERE'S AN ENVIRONMENTAL IMPACT STUDY.
ZIP

SEE, GRIMMY... THIS IS A DOG TRAINING BOOK. WHENEVER YOU HAVE A PROBLEM, A BOOK CAN ALWAYS HELP YOU SOLVE IT...

THIS BOOK WILL HELP US HOUSEBREAK REXXON IF HE STARTS TO HAVE ANOTHER ACCIDENT...

© 1989 Grimmy Inc. Distributed By Tribune Media Services
LIKE RIGHT NOW?
5-20

HEY, IT WORKS!

MUMMY DOESN'T WANT WIDOW PUPPY TO USE HER FLOWERS AS HIS LITTER-BOX...OK? NOW, GO OUT AND PWAY.

OH, GRIMMY.. I THINK LITTLE REXXON HAS FINALLY LEARNED WHAT THE YARD IS FOR...
YIP YIP YIP!
5-26
© 1989 Grimmy Inc.
Distributed By Tribune Media Services

..YEAH, HIDING.
WHOOSH

YES, YES... I'D LOVE TO SEE A FREE DEMONSTRATION.
BRUSHES
© 1989 Grimmy Inc.
Distributed By Tribune Media Services
5-27

OK, LADY... I'M HERE FOR THE CLEAN-UP.
© 1989 Grimmy Inc.
Distributed By Tribune Media Services

YUCK... I DON'T KNOW, THIS RUG LOOKS AWFULLY GRIM.

SEE, ALREADY I'M BEING BLAMED.
5-29

LET ME REASSURE YOU THAT REXXON PROMISES TO EVENTUALLY CLEAN UP THIS MESS HE'S MADE...

BUT IT'S GOING TO TAKE TIME, AS SOON AS HE GOES THROUGH THE PROPER CHANNELS.
5-30

CHANNELS ?! WHAT CHANNELS?
© 1989 Grimmy Inc.
Distributed By Tribune Media Services

WELL, RIGHT NOW HE'S WORKING ON THE DISNEY CHANNEL...
CLICK

THERE'S GOOD NEWS AND BAD NEWS... FIRST THE BAD NEWS. I CAN'T GET THE STAINS OUT OF YOUR CARPET...
WHAT'S THE GOOD NEWS?
5-31

THAT STAIN LOOKS JUST LIKE ELVIS!
©1989 Grimmy Inc. Distributed By Tribune Media Services

MY CLIENT, REXXON, FEELS VERY, VERY BAD ABOUT THE MESS HE'S MADE.

HE KNOWS THIS CLEAN-UP IS GOING TO COST A LOT OF MONEY, AND HE WOULD LIKE TO HELP...
© 1989 Grimmy Inc. Distributed By Tribune Media Services
AND WHERE IS HE GOING TO GET THE MONEY?

HE WANTS YOU TO GIVE HIM AN ALLOWANCE.
6-1

HERE'S YOUR BILL, LADY.
6-2
© 1989 Grimmy Inc. Distributed By Tribune Media Services

650 DOLLARS FOR CARPET CLEANING? WHO'S GOING TO PAY FOR THIS?

"REXXON" IS SUCH AN APPROPRIATE NAME FOR THIS LITTLE MONGREL...

REXXON... I KNOW YOU'D LIKE TO SWEEP THIS WHOLE THING UNDER THE RUG...
© 1989 Grimmy Inc. Distributed By Tribune Media Services

BUT THE RUG IS STUCK TO THE FLOOR!!!
6-3

6-5
ATTILA
THE OL' JACK-IN-THE-LITTER-BOX TRICK, GETS'EM EVERY TIME.
©1989 Grimmy Inc.
Distributed By Tribune Media Services

HEY, GRIMMY... COME AND SEE THIS GREAT COMEDY, "THE SEVEN-YEAR ITCH."
©1989 Grimmy Inc.
Distributed By Tribune Media Services

6-6
IT SOUNDS LIKE A HORROR MOVIE TO ME.

©1989 Grimmy Inc.
Distributed By Tribune Media Services
MANGE FINALLY MADE IT AS THE MOVIE DISEASE-OF-THE-WEEK...

©1989 Grimmy Inc.
Distributed By Tribune Media Services
6-8

I ALWAYS BRUSH AFTER EVERY TRASH BAG.

!
6-9

© 1989 Grimmy Inc.
Distributed By Tribune Media Services

TV DINNER.

IT SAYS HERE THAT OVER TIME PET OWNERS AND THEIR PETS BEGIN TO LOOK ALIKE...
© 1989 Grimmy Inc.
Distributed By Tribune Media Services

YOU LUCKY DOG!
6-10

GRIMMY... DO YOU THINK I SHOULD GET A FACE-LIFT?
6/12
© 1989 Grimmy Inc.
Distributed By Tribune Media Services

SURE... I WONDER WHAT THE BULGARIAN WEIGHT LIFTING TEAM IS DOING?

WHAT IS IT, GRIMMY DO YOU WANT SOME OF THESE COOKIES?
6-13
© 1989 Grimmy Inc.
Distributed By Tribune Media Services

READ MY LIPS.

GRIMMY, YOU CANNOT SLEEP ON MY BED!!!

.. NOT IF YOU KEEP YELLING ABOUT IT, I CAN'T.

© 1989 Grimmy Inc.
Distributed By Tribune Media Services
6-15
WHAT DO YOU KNOW, THERE ARE 1000 SHEETS ON A ROLL.

FINALLY, A SELF-HELP BOOK I CAN RELATE TO...

6-16
.. GARBAGE WITHOUT GUILT.

Z

SQUEAK!

CRASH

HELL HATH NO FURY LIKE A HIGH-DECIBEL SQUEAK TOY.

ARE YOU SURE I'M PRE-SHRUNK?
BATH
SOAP
© 1989 Grimmy Inc.
Distributed By Tribune Media Services
6/19

SIT!
HEEL!
STAY!

© 1989 Grimmy Inc.
Distributed By Tribune Media Services
I HATE RUNNING INTO MY OLD OBEDIENCE SCHOOL TEACHER...
6-20

RETAIL SHOP
© 1989 Grimmy Inc.
Distributed By Tribune Media Services
OUCH!
6/21

WHAP

© 1989 Grimmy Inc.
Distributed By Tribune Media Services
YUCK, GRIMM!

ANYONE CAN BLOW A KISS... IT TAKES REAL TALENT TO BLOW A LICK.
6/22

GEE, THIS DOG FOOD MAKES ITS OWN GRAVY WHEN YOU ADD WATER.
7/3
GRIM

WHAT A CONVENIENT AND TIME-SAVING HELP FOR ANY HOMEMAKER...
GRIM

© 1989 Grimmy Inc.
Distributed By Tribune Media Services

DOMESTICATED, I'M BECOMING DOMESTICATED.

GOSH, MY DOGGY DISH IS SO SPARKLING CLEAN, I CAN ALMOST SEE MY FACE IN IT...
7-4
© 1989 Grimmy Inc.
Distributed By Tribune Media Services

..WHEN YOU'RE DOMESTICATED, LITTLE THINGS TURN YOU ON.

GRIMMY, WHAT'S WRONG WITH YOU?...
7-5

ARE YOU SICK? ARE YOU HUNGRY?

I'M DOMESTICATED.
YOU'RE WEIRD.
© 1989 Grimmy Inc.
Distributed By Tribune Media Services

I CAN'T BELIEVE IT. SHE'S BRAINWASHED ME...

I'VE BECOME DOMESTICATED. I HAVE NO WILL OF MY OWN.
© 1989 Grimmy Inc.
Distributed By Tribune Media Services

I DO TRICKS ON COMMAND, I COME WHEN CALLED... I'M A ZOMBIE...
7-6

...I'M THE DOG OF THE LIVING DEAD.

I'M NOT DOMESTICATED, I'M STILL THE WILD, SAVAGE, PRIMITIVE BEAST...

WHO COULD ESCAPE INTO THE WILDERNESS ANYTIME I WANTED TO...

...JUST BY BITING DOWN ON THIS LEASH WITH MY FEROCIOUS TEETH...
© 1989 Grimmy Inc.
Distributed By Tribune Media Services

...BUT I DON'T WANT TO BREAK MY CAPS.
7-7

I'LL PROVE I'M NOT DOMESTICATED, I'M GOING TO START LIVING ON THE EDGE.
7-8

JUST ME AGAINST NATURE, ROUGHING IT, BRAVING THE ELEMENTS...
© 1989 Grimmy Inc.
Distributed By Tribune Media Services

THERE... I'VE UNPLUGGED MY ELECTRIC BLANKET.

I WISH I COULD BE LIKE CARL THE WONDER POODLE. HE'S SO COOL.

OF COURSE... I'M NOT SO BAD MYSELF.
© 1989 Grimmy Inc.
Distributed By Tribune Media Services
7-10

IN FACT, AT TIMES, I LOOK LIKE THE CLOSEST THING TO BURT REYNOLDS...

..HIS TOUPEE.

OH, BOY... TODAY'S EPISODE IS REALLY EXCITING...

CARL THE WONDER DOG HAS A CAT, TWO AMWAY DISTRIBUTORS AND A MARY KAY SALESMAN TREED IN HIS FRONT YARD...

CARL IS MY KIND OF GUY...
7-11
© 1989 Grimmy Inc.
Distributed By Tribune Media Services

I MEAN IT, GRIMMY, IF YOU KEEP WATCHING TELEVISION LIKE THAT...

...YOU'LL TURN IN-TO A TV SET.

© 1989 Grimmy Inc.
Distributed By Tribune Media Services
7-12

IT MUST BE FUN TO BE A BIG STAR LIKE CARL THE WONDER POODLE...

YOU CAN TELL HE HAS BECOME A REALLY BIG STAR...
© 1989 Grimmy Inc.
Distributed By Tribune Media Services

...HE GOT AN UNLISTED DOG TAG.
7/13

CARL THE WONDER POODLE IS MY HERO.
7/14

I WANT TO BE JUST LIKE HIM...
© 1989 Grimmy Inc.
Distributed By Tribune Media Services

...EXCEPT FOR THE WAY HE STAINS THE RUG WHENEVER HE GETS EXCITED.

OH, BOY.. TODAY CARL THE WONDER POODLE IS PLAYING A FAMOUS HOLLYWOOD TV DOG...
7-15

BUT ALL OF THE DOGS WRITERS HAVE GONE ON STRIKE BECAUSE OF BAD WORKING CONDITIONS...

SO, FOR THE LAST HALF HOUR, CARL HAS JUST STOOD THERE WAGGING HIS TAIL...
© 1989 Grimmy Inc.
Distributed By Tribune Media Services

... HOW DO THEY KEEP COMING UP WITH THESE GREAT PLOTS ?

NOW, WHERE IS THAT DOG? I TOLD HIM TO TAKE OUT THE TRASH BAG HOURS AGO...
..FIRST, I THOUGHT WE'D GO TO TONY'S FOR PASTA..THEN ON TO A BISTRO FOR COCKTAILS AND DANCING,
© 1989 Grimmy Inc.
Distributed By Tribune Media Services

I'VE DIED AND GONE TO HEAVEN.
REDWOOD NATIONAL FOREST
7/18
© 1989 Grimmy Inc.
Distributed By Tribune Media Services

LOOK WHAT I GOT, GRIMMY.. ISN'T HE ADORABLE? IT'S A FAT, LITTLE PARROT...
WHAT SHOULD WE CALL HIM?
.. POLY-UNSATURATED,
© 1989 Grimmy Inc.
Distributed By Tribune Media Services
7-19

CAN YOU BELIEVE THERE ARE PEOPLE WHO ACTUALLY EAT SNAILS COOKED IN GARLIC AND BUTTER?...

..I MEAN THEY'RE SO GOOD RAW.
© 1989 Grimmy Inc.
Distributed By Tribune Media Services
7/20

Café
WAITER, I'D LIKE TO ORDER DINNER FOR ONE.. DO YOU TAKE PLASTIC?
7/21

DOG
© 1989 Grimmy Inc. Distributed By Tribune Media Services

QUICK, ATTILA.. THE GOOSE IS COMING IN THE DOOR. JUST SMILE AND ACT LIKE WE HAVEN'T DONE ANYTHING WRONG...

© 1989 Grimmy Inc. Distributed By Tribune Media Services
7-22

.. BUT WE HAVEN'T DONE ANYTHING WRONG.
WHAT-EVER.

FLEAS.. THIS DOG GAVE ME HIS FLEAS!!!
GEE.. IT'S LIKE A BUG DAY CARE CENTER.

THEY'RE ALL OVER ME...
NOW, KIDS, YOU BE NICE.

AUGGH
DON'T GIVE THEM ANY SNACKS AND HAVE THEM IN BED BY NINE...
© 1989 Grimmy Inc. Distributed By Tribune Media Services
4-8

I USUALLY LET THEM STAY UP TO WATCH COSBY.

WHAT'S A SIX-LETTER PHRASE FOR THINKING YOU'VE DONE SOMETHING BEFORE?...
DEJA VU.
CROSS WORD
© 1989 Grimmy Inc. Distributed By Tribune Media Services
8/14

WHAT'S A SIX-LETTER PHRASE FOR THINKING YOU'VE DONE SOMETHING BEFORE?...
!
CROSS WORD

SUMMER TIME, SUMMER TIME, SUM, SUM A SUMMER TIME...

SUMMER TIME, SUMMER TIME, SUM, SUM, A SUMMER TI...
8/15

!

NOT YET!! DO YOU HEAR ME? NOT YET!!

MINE... EVERYTHING IS MINE.. EVERYTHING THAT FALLS ON THE FLOOR BELONGS TO ME...

SHOES, SOCKS, CANDY, DONUTS, BUBBLE GUM, TABLE SCRAPS, MINE, ALL MINE...
8-16

GRIMM, DO YOU REALLY THINK THAT OWNING A LOT OF STUFF IS GOING TO MAKE YOU HAPPY?

...NOTHING SUCCEEDS LIKE EXCESS.

MINE, EVERYTHING ON THE FLOOR IS MINE, I OWN IT... IT BELONGS TO ME.

GO ON... DROP SOMETHING ON THE FLOOR, ANYTHING, JUST DROP IT, AND SEE WHAT HAPPENS...

I'LL GRAB IT.. BECAUSE IT'S MY PROPERTY. I OWN IT. I OWN EVERYTHING DOWN HERE.. IT'S MINE, ALL MINE.
8-17

I FEEL LIKE I'M LIVING WITH DONALD TRUMP.

ATTILA, JUST SO THERE'S NO CONFUSION ABOUT WHOSE PROPERTY IS WHOSE AROUND HERE...

I'VE TAKEN THE LIBERTY OF LABELING OUR WATER BOWLS...

SEE?... THIS ONE IS MY WATER BOWL...
DOG
8-18

GRIMM!!
CAT

8/19
WHOOPS,,,
CHOMP
HEY, THAT WAS MY DINNER ROLL YOU JUST ATE!
GULP
JUST THINK OF IT AS A HOSTILE TAKEOVER.
© 1989 Grimmy Inc.
Distributed By Tribune Media Services

YOU FLEAS HAVE BEEN A GREAT AUDIENCE...I WISH I COULD TAKE YOU ALL HOME WITH ME...
WHOOSH
© 1989 Grimmy Inc.
Distributed By Tribune Media Services
8/21
SCRATCH SCRATCH SCRATCH
WHY... WHY CAN'T I KEEP MY BIG MOUTH SHUT?

YUCK, GRIMM, GET OFF MY BED!!

YOU'VE GOT OVER FIFTY FLEAS LIVING ON YOUR BACK!!!

FIFTY?!

© 1989 Grimmy Inc.
Distributed By Tribune Media Services
YOU MEAN I'VE GONE CONDO?
8-22

I DON'T BELIEVE IT. SHE SAID I WAS FILTHY AND I WAS COVERED IN FLEAS.

AND THEN SHE CALLED ME A THIRD-RATE FLEA MOTEL!
8-23
© 1989 Grimmy Inc.
Distributed By Tribune Media Services

DO YOU KNOW WHAT THIS MEANS I'M GOING TO HAVE TO DO?
TAKE A BATH?

...ADD A POOL AND PUT IN A SATELLITE DISH.
GESH.

HOW, ATTILA... HOW COULD THIS HAPPEN TO ME?
8-24

ONE MINUTE I'M JUST AN AVERAGE, NORMAL, HAPPY-GO-LUCKY DOG..
© 1989 Grimmy Inc.
Distributed By Tribune Media Services

..THE NEXT MINUTE I'M A LOW-INCOME HOUSING PROJECT! HOW? HOW?

MAYBE YOUR FLEAS KNOW SOMEONE AT HUD.

I CAN'T UNDERSTAND WHY PEOPLE DON'T LIKE FLEAS? THEY MAKE GREAT PETS.

THEY'RE QUIET, FAITHFUL, EASY TO TAKE CARE OF, THEY'D FOLLOW YOU ANYWHERE ...
© 1989 Grimmy Inc.
Distributed By Tribune Media Services

YOU CAN OWN AS MANY AS YOU WANT AND THEY DON'T COST YOU ANY MONEY ...
8-25

..THE BEST THINGS IN LIFE ARE FLEAS.

YUCK... GET OUT OF HERE, FLIES.
GRIM
© 1989 Grimmy Inc.
Distributed By Tribune Media Services
8/26

BYE, KIDS. I'LL BE BACK LATER.

QUICK, SHE'S GONE... NOW'S OUR CHANCE, ATTILA... THE VACUUM CLEANER IS ASLEEP!

THE ONLY TIME YOU CAN DESTROY A VACUUM IS WHEN IT'S LYING DORMANT.
10/30

TELL ME, WHY DO WE WANT TO DESTROY THE VACUUM?
IF YOU LEAVE THEM ALONE THEY START TO MULTIPLY.

HEY, WHAT LUCK.. HERE'S A ROPE ATTACHED TO THE VACUUM, YOU TIE HIM UP...
10-31

AND I'LL STICK THE OTHER END TO THE WALL SO IT CAN'T RUN AWAY.

© 1989 Grimmy Inc.
Distributed By Tribune Media Services

ZIT

BRRRRRRRRRRR
SMART MOVE, DR. FRANKENSTEIN

DUM DUM, DUM DUM, DUM DUM...
11-1

© 1989 Grimmy Inc.
Distributed By Tribune Media Services
DID YOU HEAR SOMETHING?
NO.
ME NEITHER.

BRRRAAAAAAAAAAAPP

IT'S SHAMU THE KILLER VACUUM...

THINK OF SOMETHING, QUICK.

I COMMAND YOU TO STOP!
© 1989 Grimmy Inc.
Distributed By Tribune Media Services
11-2

GARLIC, I'LL TRY GARLIC.

WE'VE GOT TO HIDE FROM THAT VACUUM CLEANER, QUICK.. IN HERE...

WHEW, THAT WAS CLOSE... GEEZ, IT'S DARK IN HERE.... TURN ON THE LIGHT.

CLICK
A BROOM CLOSET!!
© 1989 Grimmy Inc.
Distributed By Tribune Media Services
11-3

IT'S THE VACUUM BREEDING GROUND.

ATTILA WE NEED EQUIPMENT IF WE'RE GOING TO FIGHT THAT VACUUM CLEANER.

ROPE... WOODEN STAKE... PLIERS.. SCREW DRIVER... POWDERED DONUTS...

© 1989 Grimmy Inc.
Distributed By Tribune Media Services

POWDERED DONUTS?

EVEN INDIANA JONES HAS TO EAT.

© 1989 Grimmy Inc.
Distributed By Tribune Media Services

AAAAAAAAAAAA
A AAAA
11-6

BRRRRRRRRR
RRRR

IT'S THE NIGHT OF THE LIVING VACUUM.

HERE COMES THE VACUUM FROM HELL...

I THINK IT WANTS A SACRIFICE.
© 1989 Grimmy Inc.
Distributed By Tribune Media Services

...WHERE'S A VIRGIN WOOL CARPET WHEN YOU NEED ONE?
11-7

IT'S CHASING US... LET'S RUN IN THE BATHROOM AND DUMP IT IN THE TOILET.

© 1989 Grimmy Inc.
Distributed By Tribune Media Services
GOOD, NOW START FLUSHING AND LET'S DROWN THIS THING...
FLUSH... GLUG... GLUG
GLUG GLUG GLUG GLUG..
OH OH.. IT'S JUST GETTING BIGGER... I THINK WE'VE INVENTED THE FIRST ELECTRIC WATER BALLOON.
11-8

THE VACUUM IS GROWING BIGGER AND BIGGER BY THE MINUTE...
GLUG GLUG

IT'S DRINKING UP ALL THE WATER IN THE TOILET.

WE'VE GOT TO DO SOMETHING BEFORE IT DESTROYS THE HOUSE...
© 1989 Grimmy Inc.
Distributed By Tribune Media Services

WHY DO I FEEL LIKE I'M IN A GODZILLA MOVIE?
11-9

LOOK OUT... THE VACUUM IS FILLING UP WITH WATER
11-10

SPLOIT
© 1989 Grimmy Inc.
Distributed By Tribune Media Services

OH, SWELL... NOW WE'VE MADE IT MAD.

OH, OH... IT'S GETTING CLOSER AND CLOSER...
11-11

SLURP
© 1989 Grimmy Inc.
Distributed By Tribune Media Services

GRIMMY.. WHERE ARE YOU?
DON'T ASK.

MIRROR... DO YOU THINK I'M ATTRACTIVE?

MZ. GOOSE... I CAN'T BELIEVE SOMEONE WHO LOOKS LIKE YOU IS UNATTACHED....
...... TO A LIFE SUPPORT SYSTEM.
11-13

CAREFUL... I, THINK THERE'S A DOG LEG TO THE LEFT.
11-14
© 1989 Grimmy Inc. Distributed By Tribune Media Services
FLEAS AT GOLF

© 1989 Grimmy Inc. Distributed By Tribune Media Services
MOO...
11-15
BEAUTY AND THE WILDEBEEST

HEY... NO KIDDING, I'M FROM IDAHO TOO!
11-16
© 1989 Grimmy Inc. Distributed By Tribune Media Services

© 1989 Grimmy Inc. Distributed By Tribune Media Services
HERE COMES THE SUN.... HERE COMES THE SUN....
11-17

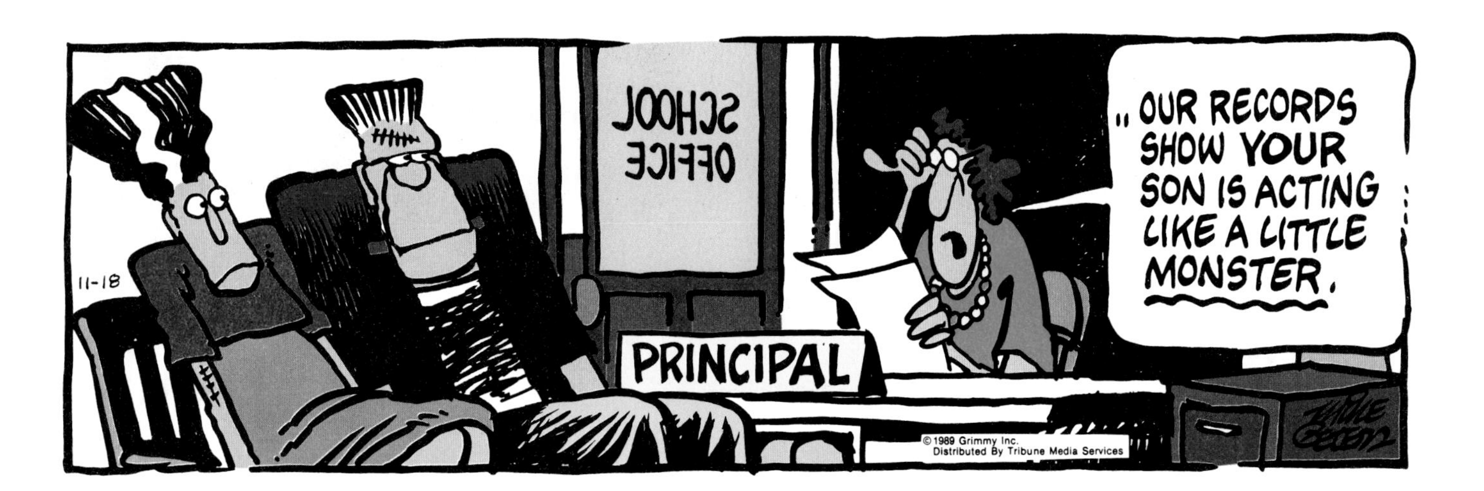
11-18
SCHOOL OFFICE
PRINCIPAL
"..OUR RECORDS SHOW YOUR SON IS ACTING LIKE A LITTLE MONSTER."
©1989 Grimmy Inc. Distributed By Tribune Media Services

MMMM... WHAT IS IT, GRIMMY?
I JUST OPENED CLUB MUTT, MY NEW FIVE-STAR FLEA MOTEL...

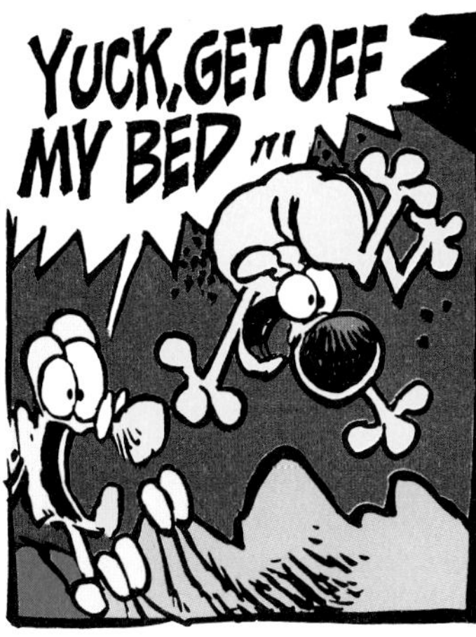
YUCK, GET OFF MY BED...

YOU'RE COVERED IN FLEAS FROM YOUR HEAD TO YOUR TAIL...
©1989 Grimmy Inc. Distributed By Tribune Media Services

THAT'S NOT MY TAIL..THAT'S THE PRESIDENTIAL SUITE.
12/18

WELCOME TO CLUB MUTT, EVERYBODY.

©1989 Grimmy Inc. Distributed By Tribune Media Services
I HOPE YOU INSECTS HAVE A NICE DAY...
12-19

AND IF YOU NEED ANYTHING... JUST BUZZ.

SOMETIMES I JUST CRACK ME UP...
HEH HEH HEH HEH

ATTILA..MY FLEA MOTEL IS ALL FILLED UP...

I'VE GOT A CONVENTION OF CARPENTER ANTS COMING TONIGHT AND I NEED HELP.
©1989 Grimmy Inc. Distributed By Tribune Media Services

SO, WHY ARE YOU TELLING ME?
12-20

HAVE YOU EVER THOUGHT ABOUT A CAREER IN HOTEL MANAGEMENT?

I LOVE BEING A FLEA MOTEL ...
12-21

RUMBLERUMBLERUMBLE

BUT I NEVER SHOULD'VE INSTALLED THOSE VIBRATING BEDS.

OH OH ... MY FLEA MOTEL IS TOTALLY FULL.
12 22

I CAN'T TAKE ANY MORE BUGS.

MAYBE I SHOULD TURN ON A "NO VACANCY" SIGN.

NO... THAT WOULD JUST ATTRACT FLYS.

ATTILA, I'VE GOT SOMETHING VERY PERSONAL I'VE BEEN CARRYING AROUND, THAT I'D LIKE TO SHARE WITH YOU.
SURE. WHAT IS IT?

FLEAS!

MERRY CHRISTMAS.
12-23

I GOT A FIR FOR CHRISTMAS.
12-25

Y'KNOW...SOMETIMES I QUESTION IF THERE REALLY IS A DOG.
12-26
©1989 Grimmy Inc.
Distributed By Tribune Media Services
AGNOSTIC FLEAS
V GOOD

IT'S DINNER TIME, GRIMMY, WHAT CAN I FIX YOU?
GRI
©1989 Grimmy Inc.
Distributed By Tribune Media Services

NEVER MENTION "ME" AND "FIX" IN THE SAME BREATH.
12/27
GR

I SENTENCE YOU TO 30 DAYS IN AN INVISIBLE BOX.
12-28
©1989 Grimmy Inc.
Distributed By Tribune Media Services
MIME COURT

STOP THAT... I HAVEN'T EVEN GOTTEN TO THE SCARY PART YET.
©1989 Grimmy Inc.
Distributed By Tribune Media Services
12-29
WHEN ROLY-POLYS CAMP OUT

WHY CARTOONISTS DIDN'T LIVE LONG IN THE OLD WEST

THE LOIS AND CLARK EXPEDITION

GRIMMY, YOU'VE BEEN STANDING THERE WATCHING ME EAT FOR THE LAST HALF HOUR...
©1990 Grimmy Inc.
Distributed By Tribune Media Services

HERE, BECAUSE I'M A KIND, WARM HEARTED PERSON, I'LL GIVE YOU ONE OF MY FRENCH FRIES...

THANK YOU, MOTHER TERESA.
1/4

GRIMMY... WILL YOU STOP BEGGING AT THE TABLE, I ALREADY GAVE YOU PART OF MY DINNER...
1/5

SEE? I PUT A WHOLE FRENCH FRY DOWN ON THE FLOOR...
©1990 Grimmy Inc.
Distributed By Tribune Media Services
OH WOW, LOOK AT THE SIZE OF THAT THING.

GRIMMY...STOP LOOKING AT ME WITH THOSE BIG SAD EYES OF YOURS.
I CAN'T EAT MY FOOD WITH YOU STARING LIKE THAT.
©1990 Grimmy Inc.
Distributed By Tribune Media Services
THAT'S THE IDEA.
1/6

LOOK AT THIS "BENJI" MOVIE, GRIMMY...ISN'T HE SWEET?
EVEN THOUGH HE'S COLD AND HUNGRY, HE GAVE THAT LITTLE KITTEN HIS LAST BIT OF FOOD...
©1990 Grimmy Inc.
Distributed By Tribune Media Services
GAG!
AIR SICK BAG
1/8

© 1990 Grimmy Inc.
Distributed By Tribune Media Services
WHY DO I ALWAYS GO FOR TALLER WOMEN?
1/9

© 1990 Grimmy Inc.
Distributed By Tribune Media Services
CHAMPAGNE WISHES AND CAVIAR DREAMS...
1/10
ROBIN LEECH

ZOO
WHOA...I JUST HAVE LINT IN MINE...
KANGAROO
1/11
© 1990 Grimmy Inc.
Distributed By Tribune Media Services

© 1990 Grimmy Inc.
Distributed By Tribune Media Services
SAY THAT AGAIN, MAC..AND I'LL PUNCH YOUR LIGHTS OUT..
WHEN FIREFLIES DRINK

©1990 Grimmy Inc.
Distributed By Tribune Media Services
JUNIOR, LOOK AT THIS ROOM, ALL NEAT AND CLEAN... AND YOU CALL YOURSELF A SLOTH?
1/13

©1990 Grimmy Inc.
Distributed By Tribune Media Services
1-15

HALF THE FUN OF A CHEW TOY IS THE ANTICIPATION...

1-16

SQUEAK SQUEAK
SQUEAK SQUEAK
SQUEAK
SQUEAK
SQUEAK
SQUEAK SQUEAK
SQUEAK SQUEAK
SQUEAK SQUEAK
SQUEAK SQUEAK
©1990 Grimmy Inc.
Distributed By Tribune Media Services

I LOVE WHEN THEY SCREAM LIKE THAT.

1-17
©1990 Grimmy Inc.
Distributed By Tribune Media Services

I'VE GOT TO GET DECAFFEINATED.

1-18

YOW...
©1990 Grimmy Inc.
Distributed By Tribune Media Services

HELL HAS NO FURY LIKE AN ANGRY CHEW TOY...

1-19

YIPE...
©1990 Grimmy Inc.
Distributed By Tribune Media Services

GRIMMY, ARE YOU OKAY?
DEFINE, "OKAY".

WHAT ARE YOU DOING WITH THAT CHEW TOY, GRIMM?
SHHH, WATCH THIS.
1-20

©1990 Grimmy Inc.
Distributed By Tribune Media Services

DID YOU SEE THAT, HUH? HUH?

GRIMM, WHEN WAS YOUR LAST DISTEMPER SHOT?

1/29
INTERESTING DIP, GRIMMY. WHAT IS IT? ONION DIP? SOUR CREAM AND CHIVE DIP?...
POTATO CHIPS

NO... FLEA DIP.

1/30
THE ART OF BARKING
© 1990 Grimmy Inc.
Distributed By Tribune Media Services

I JUST LOVE THESE SELF-HELP BOOKS...
THE ART OF

© 1990 Grimmy Inc.
Distributed By Tribune Media Services

SQUEEZE....
BONK
1-31

TELL HEIMLICH IT ALSO WORKS ON HAIR BALLS.

HOW COME BENJI GETS ALL THE CHICKS ...
© 1990 Grimmy Inc.
Distributed By Tribune Media Services
2-1

.. AND I GET ALL THE TICKS ?!!

EAT IT, GRIMMY, IT'S OAT BRAN AND IT'S SUPPOSED TO BE GOOD FOR YOU.
GRIN
© 1990 Grimmy Inc.
Distributed By Tribune Media Services
2-2

SNIFF
SNIFF
GRI

..AND TEN YEARS FROM NOW AN FDA REPORT WILL CALL IT A "SILENT KILLER."
GRI

2/3
HEY...I COULD GET INTO GOLF...
© 1990 Grimmy Inc. Distributed By Tribune Media Services

HI, BEAUTIFUL, WHAT'S YOUR SIGN? LET'S HIT THE HAY.
BAR
THE CHEETAH IS THE FASTEST KNOWN LAND ANIMAL
© 1990 Grimmy Inc. Distributed By Tribune Media Services
2-5

KISSES
$1.00
LICKS
2-6
© 1990 Grimmy Inc. Distributed By Tribune Media Services

RRRIINNGG... CLICK...
THIS IS YOGA HARISH, I'M OUT OF MY BODY RIGHT NOW, BUT IF YOU LEAVE YOUR NAME AND NUMBER...
© 1990 Grimmy Inc. Distributed By Tribune Media Services
2-7

VOCATIONAL COUNSELOR
2/8
SORRY, STEVE.. YOU DIDN'T SCORE WELL AS AN ELECTRICAL ENGINEER... BUT YOU'RE A GREAT SLUG...

© 1990 Grimmy Inc.
Distributed By Tribune Media Services
2-9
OKAY... ON THREE, WE DO THE WISH BONE FORMATION..

2-10
© 1990 Grimmy Inc.
Distributed By Tribune Media Services
YOU'RE GOING TO FRY FOR THIS, DUMPTY, AND I MEAN FRY...

VALENTINES, I NEVER GET ANY VALENTINES.

WHAT'S WRONG WITH ME ?
2-12

EVERY TIME I MEET A GIRL, SHE LEAVES ME FOR SOMEONE ELSE...

I THOUGHT ONLY TRASH GETS DUMPED ONCE A WEEK.

WHOA... LOOK AT THAT CUTE LITTLE SHEEP DOG.

I'VE NEVER SEEN HER AROUND HERE BEFORE.

2-13

OKAY, GRIMMY.. IT'S TIME TO TURN ON THE CHARM... BE COOL... BE SUAVE...

IT'S HARD TO BE SUAVE WHEN YOUR TAIL IS WAGGING.

WELL, IT'S TIME TO MEET THE GIRL OF MY DREAMS.

HI, BEAUTIFUL.

MY NAME IS GRIMMY. SOMETIMES WORMS GIVE ME DIARRHEA.

GIRLS LOVE IT WHEN YOU SHARE YOUR FEELINGS...
2/14

NOW THAT I'VE BROKEN THE ICE, I NEED TO KEEP THE CONVERSATION GOING...

QUICK, SAY SOMETHING. COMPLIMENT HER, BUT DON'T GET TOO PERSONAL...
2-15

YOU DON'T DROOL MUCH FOR A SHEEP DOG.

SMOOTH, GRIMM... REAL, REAL SMOOTH.

I CAN'T BELIEVE THAT LITTLE SHEEP DOG IS GOING OUT WITH ME...
2-16

I WONDER IF SHE THINKS I'M ATTRACTIVE?

SURE, I'VE GAINED A FEW POUNDS, BUT I'M NOT FAT...

...THESE ARE JUST PUPPY-LOVE HANDLES!

3-5
LOOK...I JUST CAUGHT A BUG...IT'S ONE OF THOSE BIG ONES WITH THE SPOTS ON HIS BACK... NOW DON'T TELL ME, I KNOW WHAT IT'S CALLED, UM...UM...OH, IT'S JUST ON THE TIP OF MY TONGUE...

3-6
LEANING TOWER →
HONEY...DO YOU WANT ME TO PICK UP A PISA ON THE WAY HOME?

GRIMM
I THINK SHE NEEDS TO CHANGE MY WATER.
3-7

3-8
JUNIOR...WE THINK YOU'RE OLD ENOUGH TO KNOW THAT ALL THOSE YEARS YOUR FATHER WAS ACTUALLY THE TOOTH FAIRY...

HERB... YOU'VE GOT YOUR LEFT-HAND TURN SIGNAL ON AGAIN...
3-9

3-10
STATE HOSPITAL
I HATE PICKING UP THESE CRAZY QUILTS!

IT'S LOTTO TIME, MZ. GOOSE,
GOOD, I'VE GOT MY NUMBER WRITTEN DOWN RIGHT HERE,

...AND THIS WEEK'S 35 MILLION DOLLAR SUPER LOTTO WINNING NUMBER IS...

18 9 9 61 80 11

NOTHING ON MINE, HOW 'BOUT YOURS?
3-12

MY 35 MILLION DOLLAR WINNING LOTTO TICKET WAS RIGHT HERE ON THE COUNTER,

SOMEBODY MUST HAVE THROWN IT AWAY!!!
3-13

CALM DOWN.. IF IT WAS ACCIDENTALLY THROWN AWAY.. I'M SURE IT'S PERFECTLY SAFE RIGHT THERE IN THE KITCHEN TRASH CAN.
!

MUNCH, MUNCH, MUNCH, CHEW GULP.
THE PLOT THICKENS...

HE DID IT.. HE ATE MY LOTTERY TICKET !!
3-14
GRIMM, HOW COULD YOU EAT A 35 MILLION DOLLAR LOTTERY TICKET ?
..WELL, FIRST YOU ADD SOME GARLIC, THEN 1/2 TSP. OF SALT...
© 1990 Grimmy Inc. Distributed By Tribune Media Services

WELL, MZ. GOOSE, WE'VE X-RAYED GRIMMY AND WE HAVE GOOD NEWS AND BAD NEWS...
WHAT'S THE BAD NEWS?
3/15
GRIMMY DID IN FACT EAT YOUR LOTTERY TICKET.
OMIGOSH, WHAT'S THE GOOD NEWS?
LOTTERY TICKETS ARE AN EXCELLENT SOURCE OF FIBER.
© 1990 Grimmy Inc. Distributed By Tribune Media Services

DOCTOR..GRIMMY JUST ATE MY WINNING LOTTERY TICKET. WHAT SHOULD I DO?
3-16
HAVE YOU CONSIDERED DYNAMITE?
...IS THE POPE CATHOLIC?
© 1990 Grimmy Inc. Distributed By Tribune Media Services

IF WE KEEP GRIMMY SUSPENDED, IT COULD CAUSE THE LODGED LOTTERY TICKET IN HIS STOMACH TO SHIFT.
?
© 1990 Grimmy Inc. Distributed By Tribune Media Services

...AND IF IT DOESN'T?

...THEN WE'LL TURN HIM INTO A PIÑATA.
3-17

LOOK, GRIMMY, WE'VE GOT TO GET THAT LOTTERY TICKET OUT OF YOUR STOMACH.
EITHER I PERFORM SURGERY ON YOU...
OR NURSE DIESEL WILL GIVE YOU A BARIUM X-RAY.
..CAN I HAVE WHAT'S BEHIND DOOR NUMBER THREE?
3-19

LOOK, GRIMMY... I'M A DESPERATE WOMAN. YOU'VE SWALLOWED MY LOTTERY TICKET AND THIS GUY MAY BE OUR ONLY HOPE...

AH ... A VOLUNTEER!!
3-20

MZ. GOOSE... YOU'VE GOT TO THINK OF SOMETHING TO GET THAT LOTTERY TICKET OUT OF GRIMMY.

LOOK, GRIMMY... I GOT YOU FIVE BENJI MOVIES, THE BEST OF GERALDO, AND A TAPE OF "A VERY BRADY CHRISTMAS."
CHOKE.. GAG
AIR SICK BAG
3-21

I CAN'T BELIEVE THAT DIRTY DOG ATE MY FORTUNE... I'M OUT 35 MILLION DOLLARS.

OH WELL... IT'S ONLY MONEY. AT LEAST I'VE STILL GOT MY HEALTH...

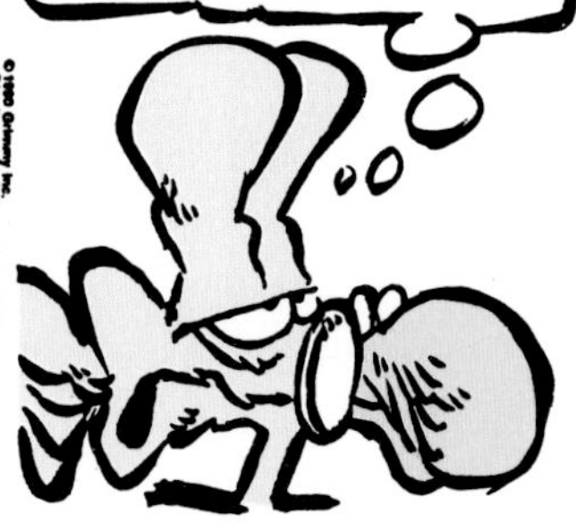
.. AND A ROOF OVER MY HEAD AND ENOUGH FOOD TO LIVE ON...

I'M STARTING TO SOUND LIKE IVANA TRUMP.
3-22

LOOK, THIS PAPER I WROTE MY LOTTERY NUMBER ON WAS UPSIDE DOWN!!!

SO...WHAT I THOUGHT WAS MY WINNING NUMBER 1899618011 WAS ONLY 1108196681.

SO, I GUESS I DON'T NEED THAT LOTTERY STUB THAT GRIMMY SWALLOWED, AFTER ALL...
3-23

..YOU CAN STOP NOW, GRIMMY.
MUNCH
GULP
FIBER
BRAN
PRUNES

WEIGHT AND FORTUNE
YOU'VE GAINED WEIGHT AND LOST A FORTUNE.
3
24

GRIMMY
TM

OTHER GRIMMY TITLES

GRIMMY POCKET BOOKS

(128 pages, black and white)

BEST IN SHOW	£1.95
SO MANY TREES, SO LITTLE TIME	£1.95
PICK OF THE LITTER	£2.25
MAKES ENDS MEET	£2.25

Take advantage of this special offer:

Buy one title at the price shown and we will pay postage and packing

Buy two books for £2.99 including postage and packing

Buy all four for £5.00 including postage and packing.

Tick the title(s) you require and send a cheque or postal order made payable to Ravette Books Limited at the following address:

GRIMMY POCKET BOOK OFFER,
Ravette Books Limited, 8 Clifford Street, London W1X 1RB

(Offer restricted to UK and Irish Republic and applies to postal sales only — not available in shops)

Name ....

Address ....

....